MY HOLIDAY RANT about...

journals with a twist

from you to me ®

Published by *from you to me* ltd

All titles are available at good gift and book shops or www.fromyoutome.com

from you to me Journals of a Lifetime
Dear Mum
Dear Dad
Dear Grandma
Dear Grandad
Dear Sister
Dear Brother
Dear Daughter
Dear Son
Dear Friend

Parent & Child
Bump to Birthday, pregnancy & first year journal
Our Story, for my daughter
Our Story, for my son
Mum to Mum – pass it on
Dear Baby, guest book

Teen & Tween
Mum & Me
Dad & Me
Rant & Rave – My School
Rant & Rave – My Holiday

Other Titles
Love Stories, anniversary & relationship journal
Cooking up Memories
Digging up Memories
Kicking off Memories
Dear Future Me
These were the Days
Christmas Present, Christmas Past

Many of these journals can be personalised online at www.fromyoutome.com

 . . . vb . . . to express opinions in an aggravated or impassioned way about someone or something . . .

Rant & Rave will inspire you to write, draw and doodle about the things you really care about.

A unique journal with a fun twist: Rave about the good bits, then twist the journal over to Rant and let off a little steam!

This fun and innovative activity book is easy to use and ideal for any holiday.

ABOUT ME

My eyes are :

My hair is :

My height is :

My shoe size is :

I'm from :

RANT PHOTO

FIRST  DAY

What I forgot :

What I didn't need on the journey :

What I did need on the journey :

Worst moment of the journey:

Initial thoughts when I arrived :

Who I wish had been with me :

 about the journey :

 **about the holiday destination :**

 **about who I went on holiday with :**

 about where I stayed :

 about someone I had to leave behind :

TRAVEL

HURRAH!

Things that make 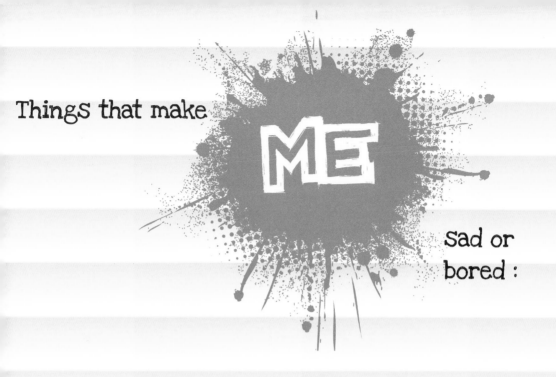 **ME**

sad or
bored :

DRAW

Some pictures of what I
got up to on my holiday :

 **about things I wanted to do but didn't get round to :**

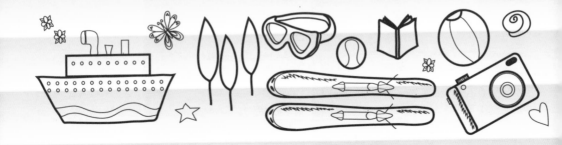

MY RANTS

Worst meal :

Saddest moment :

Most boring moment :

Earliest morning :

Worst day :

Worst experience :

RANT

about some of the conversations I had or heard :

about the worst bits :

1.

2.

3.

 **about any trips out :**

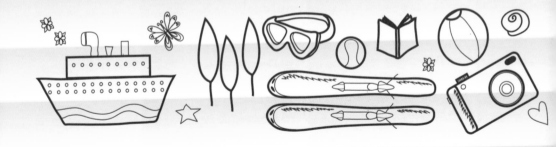

MY RANTS

Five things I wish I had brought from home :

1.

2.

3.

4.

5.

 **about the weather :**

468

WHICH WAY?

 about something that annoyed me :

 about something that didn't excite me :

 about the food and drink :

 about something I never want to do again :

468

RANT

about anything :

the worst meal :

DRAW

DRAW

the best meal :

about the worst
postcard I found:

 about anything I regret doing or saying :

 about any holiday illnesses or injuries :

 **about anything I felt was unfair :**

 **about anything I got away with :**

How I like to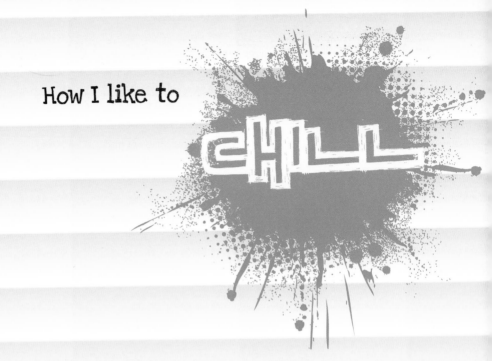

 words or letters from a magazine
to make a holiday motto :

 about games I played and lost :

the music which will remind
me of being on holiday :

WRITE in code, coloured pens or strange writing about my holiday :

TRAVEL   HURRAH!

a map of my holiday destination :

ASK Someone else to do Something on this page :

TRAVEL

HURRAH!

 **about something that hasn't improved this holiday :**

 **about this journal :**

468

WHICH WAY?

TRACE around my left hand made into :

 around my right hand made into :

OODLES OF DOODLES

OODLES OF DOODLES

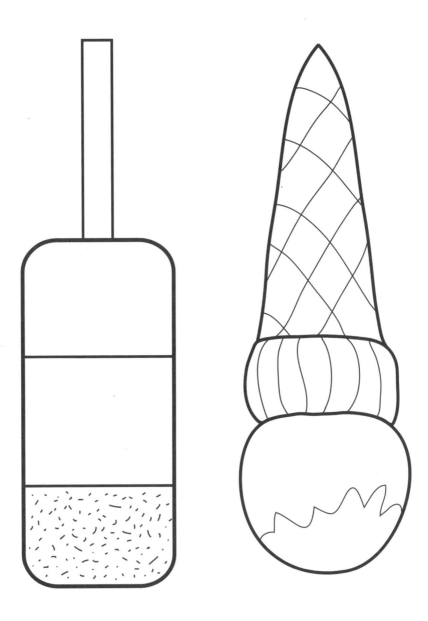

 **Something to make the hands for the clock :**

Messages I have asked people to leave me :

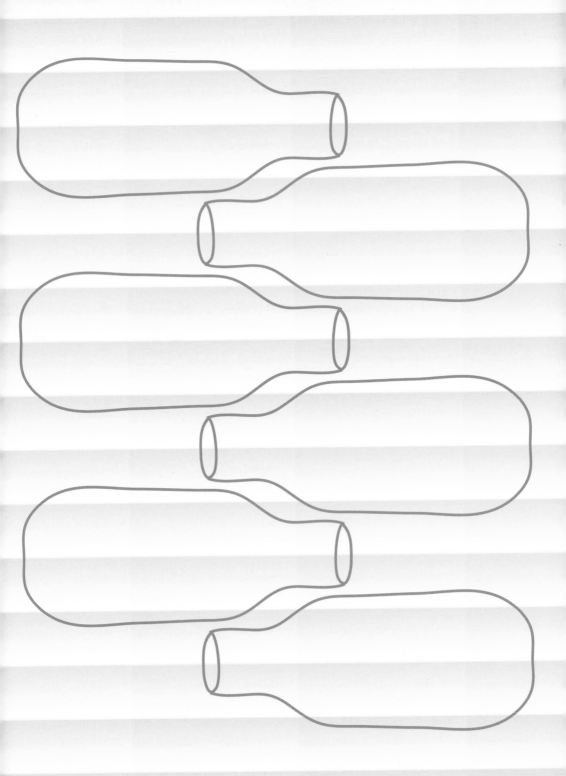

CONTACT

details of people I have met on holiday :

DESIGN

a poster to advertise this holiday :

 about something that has
improved this holiday :

 about this journal :

RAVE

about the fun things to do :

WHERE

I would like the bottle to
end up and who I would
like to discover it :

CREATE

my secret message in a
bottle :

MY RAVES

Favourite Smell :

Games I played :

How I like to

BEST
POSTCARD

RAVE

about the best
postcard I found :

DRAW

a postcard :

WRITE a postcard :

NEWS

the best piece of news
or gossip :

RAVE

about what I was allowed to do that made me feel great :

 about Something new I did :

 about how being on holiday is different :

 about any new friends I made :

 about good thoughts or dreams I
had on holiday :

MY RAVES

Things I spent my money on :

Books I read :

 a Short Story, poem or Song :

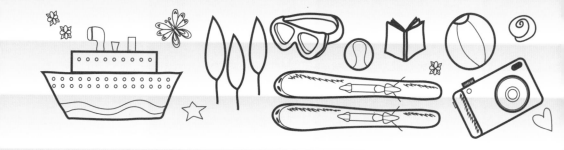

RAVE

about my top three delicious
things to eat on holiday :

1.

2.

3.

about the weather :

MY FAVES

Best meal :

Happiest moment :

Funniest moment :

Latest night :

Best day :

Best experience :

 about the things I did :

things I found on holiday :

Things that made  laugh and smile :

 about who is on holiday with me :

 a ticket :

468

WHICH WAY?

 about my holiday accommodation :

 **about my holiday destination :**

 about the journey :

MY journey DAY

Time I woke up :

What time I left :

What I wore for the journey :

What I took on the journey :

Who I was with :

RAVE PHOTO

ABOUT ME

My name is :

I like to be called :

My age is :

My height is :

My shoe size is :

Date my holiday started :

Date my holiday ended :

. . . vb . . . to express opinions with wild and extravagant enthusiasm about someone or something . . .

Rant & Rave will inspire you to write, draw and doodle about the things you really care about.

A unique journal with a fun twist: Rave about the good bits, then twist the journal over to Rant and let off a little steam!

This fun and innovative activity book is easy to use and ideal for any holiday.